Hi Slug!

and

Hug Bug

By Rebecca Colby

Illustrated by
Beatrice Tinarelli

The Letter I

Trace the lower and upper case letter with a finger. Sound out the letter.

Down,
lift,
dot

Down,
lift,
across,
lift,
across

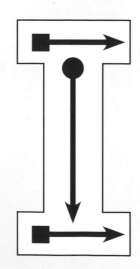

Some words to familiarise:

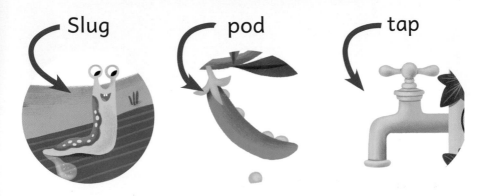

Slug

pod

tap

High-frequency words:

is   on   a

Tips for Reading 'Hi Slug!'

- Practise the words listed above before reading the story.

- If the reader struggles with any of the other words, ask them to look for sounds they know in the word. Encourage them to sound out the words and help them read the words if necessary.

- After reading the story, ask the reader how Slug said 'hi'.

Fun Activity

Build a bug hotel!

Hi Slug!

"Hi, Slug!"

Slug is on a log.

"Hi, Slug!"

Slug is on a pod.

"Hi, Slug!"

Slug is on a lid.

"Hi, Slug!"

Slug is on a tap.

"Hi, Slug!"

Slug is on a mat.

"Hi!"

The Letter G

Trace the lower and upper case letter with a finger. Sound out the letter.

Around,
up,
down,
around

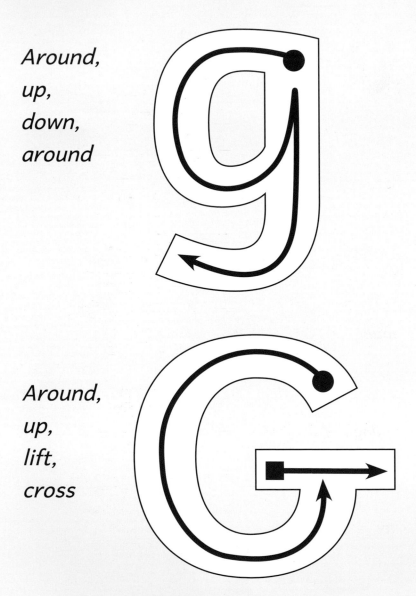

Around,
up,
lift,
cross

Some words to familiarise:

hug   mess   web

High-frequency words:

I in off up a on of

Tips for Reading 'Hug Bug'

- Practise the words listed above before reading the story.

- If the reader struggles with any of the other words, ask them to look for sounds they know in the word. Encourage them to sound out the words and help them read the words if necessary.

- After reading the story, ask the reader who hugs Slug in the end.

Fun Activity

Give someone you know a hug!

Hug Bug

Not now. I am in bed.

Not now. I am off.

23

Not now. I am a mess.

27

28

Book Bands for Guided Reading

The Institute of Education book banding system is a scale of colours that reflects the various levels of reading difficulty. The bands are assigned by taking into account the content, the language style, the layout and phonics. Word, phrase and sentence level work is also taken into consideration.

Maverick Early Readers are a bright, attractive range of books covering the pink to white bands. All of these books have been book banded for guided reading to the industry standard and edited by a leading educational consultant.

To view the whole Maverick Readers scheme, visit our website at www.maverickearlyreaders.com

Or scan the QR code above to view our scheme instantly!